Scripture Scrib

INTERMEDIATE
VOLUME I

One Another

CONCEIVED & WRITTEN BY
MARY ELLEN TEDROW-WYNN

COVER, LAYOUT DESIGN, & TYPESETTING BY
ALLISON ARMERDING

Dedication

This book is dedicated to Pastor Van, whose strong convictions
and great preaching led me to author this book.
Thank you, Pastor, for sticking to the Scriptures!

Most of all, my thanks to my Lord, who is so amazing.
I am awed at His power, His grace, and His mercy to me.
Thank you for using "such as me" for the work of Your Kingdom.

Copyright

Scripture Scribes

Scripture Scribes is copy work for students to write and fall in love with the Scriptures. Each lesson presents a verse in several English translations.

Scripture Scribes: One Another features Scripture verses from the New Testament that include the phrase "one another." Who is your "one another"?

Then one of them, a lawyer,

asked Him a question,

testing Him, and saying,

"Teacher, which is the great commandment in the law?"

Jesus said to him,

"'You shall love the Lord your God with all your heart,

with all your soul, and with all your mind.'

This is the first and great commandment.

And the second is like it:

'You shall love your neighbor as yourself.'"

Matthew 22:35-39 NKJV

Lesson 1

A new commandment I give to you, that you love one another;
as I have loved you, that you also love one another.
John 13:34 NKJV

Trace and copy the Scripture on the lines below.

A new commandment I give to you, that you love

one another; as I have loved you, that you also love

one another.

Now rewrite the verse.

A new commandment I give to you, that you love one another:
just as I have loved you, you also are to love one another.
John 13:34 ESV

Trace and copy the Scripture on the lines below.

A new commandment I give to you, that you love

one another; just as I have loved you, you also are

to love one another.

Now rewrite the verse.

A new commandment I give unto you, That ye love one another; as I have loved you, that ye also love one another.
John 13:34 KJV

Trace and copy the Scripture on the lines below.

A new commandment I give unto you, that ye love one another; as I have loved you, that ye also love one another.

Now rewrite the verse.

I give you a new command: Love each other. You must love each other as I have loved you.
John 13:34 ICB

Trace and copy the Scripture on the lines below.

I give you a new command: Love each other. You must love each other as I have loved you.

Now rewrite the verse.

commandment: a divine rule

Lesson 2

Have salt in yourselves, and have peace one with another.
Mark 9:50 KJV

Trace and copy the Scripture on the lines below.

Have salt in yourselves, and have peace

one with another.

Now rewrite the verse.

Have salt in yourselves, and have peace with one another.
Mark 9:50 NKJV

Trace and copy the Scripture on the lines below.

Have salt in yourselves, and have peace

with one another.

Now rewrite the verse.

So, be full of goodness. And have peace with each other.
Mark 9:50 ICB

Trace and copy the Scripture on the lines below.

So, be full of goodness.

And have peace with each other.

Now rewrite the verse.

Have salt in yourselves, and be at peace with one another.
Mark 9:50 ESV

Trace and copy the Scripture on the lines below.

Have salt in yourselves, and be at peace

with each other.

Now rewrite the verse.

Lesson 3

If I then, your Lord and Master, have washed your feet;
ye also ought to wash one another's feet.
John 13:14 KJV

Trace and copy the Scripture on the lines below.

If I then, your Lord and Master, have washed your

feet; ye also ought to wash one another's feet.

Now rewrite the verse.

If I then, your Lord and Teacher, have washed your feet,
you also ought to wash one another's feet.
John 13:14 NKJV

Trace and copy the Scripture on the lines below.

If I then, your Lord and Teacher, have washed your

feet, you also ought to wash one another's feet.

Now rewrite the verse.

Foot washing in Jesus' day was a task
performed by the lowliest servants.

I, your Lord and Teacher, have washed your feet.
So you also should wash each other's feet.
John 13:14 ICB

Trace and copy the Scripture on the lines below.

I, your Lord and Teacher, have washed your feet.

So you also should wash each other's feet.

Now rewrite the verse.

If I then, your Lord and Teacher, have washed your feet,
you also ought to wash one another's feet.
John 13:14 ESV

Trace and copy the Scripture on the lines below.

If I then, your Lord and Teacher, have washed your

feet, you also ought to wash one another's feet.

Now rewrite the verse.

Lesson 4

By this shall all men know that ye are my disciples,
if ye have love one to another.
John 13:35 KJV

Trace and copy the Scripture on the lines below.

By this shall all men know that ye are my disciples

if ye have love one to another.

Now rewrite the verse.

By this all will know that you are My disciples,
if you have love for one another.
John 13:35 NKJV

Trace and copy the Scripture on the lines below.

By this all will know that you are My disciples,

if you have love for one another.

Now rewrite the verse.

*All people will know that you are my followers
if you love each other.
John 13:35 ICB*

Trace and copy the Scripture on the lines below.

*All people will know that you are my followers if you
love one another.*

Now rewrite the verse.

*By this all people will know that you are my disciples,
if you have love for one another.
John 13:35 ESV*

Trace and copy the Scripture on the lines below.

*By this all people will know that you are my disciples
if you have love for one another.*

Now rewrite the verse.

Lesson 5

This is my commandment,
That ye love one another, as I have loved you.
John 15:12 KJV

Trace and copy the Scripture on the lines below.

This is my commandment, That ye love one another

as I have loved you.

Now rewrite the verse.

This is My commandment,
that you love one another as I have loved you.
John 15:12 NKJV

Trace and copy the Scripture on the lines below.

This is My commandment, that you love one another

as I have loved you.

Now rewrite the verse.

This is my command:
Love each other as I have loved you.
John 15:12 ICB

Trace and copy the Scripture on the lines below.

This is my command: Love each other as I have

loved you.

Now rewrite the verse.

This is my commandment,
that you love one another as I have loved you.
John 15:12 ESV

Trace and copy the Scripture on the lines below.

...This is my commandment, that you love one another

as I have loved you.

Now rewrite the verse.

Lesson 6

These things I command you, that ye love one another.
John 15:17 KJV

Trace and copy the Scripture on the lines below.

These things I command you,

, that ye love one another.

Now rewrite the verse.

These things I command you, that you love one another.
John 15:17 NKJV

Trace and copy the Scripture on the lines below.

These things I command you,

that you love one another.

Now rewrite the verse.

This is my command: Love each other.
John 15:17 ICB

Trace and copy the Scripture on the lines below.

This is my command: ....

Love each other.

Now rewrite the verse.

These things I command you, so that you will love one another.
John 15:17 ESV

Trace and copy the Scripture on the lines below.

...These things I command you,

so that you will love one another.

Now rewrite the verse.

Lesson 7

So we, being many, are one body in Christ,
and every one members one of another.
Romans 12:5 KJV

Trace and copy the Scripture on the lines below.

So we, being many, are one body in Christ and

every one members one of another.

Now rewrite the verse.

So we, being many, are one body in Christ,
and individually members of one another.
Romans 12:5 NKJV

Trace and copy the Scripture on the lines below.

So we, being many, are one body in Christ, and

individually members of one another.

Now rewrite the verse.

In the same way, we are many,
but in Christ we are all one body.
Romans 12:5 ICB

Trace and copy the Scripture on the lines below.

In the same way, we are many, but in Christ

we are all one body.

Now rewrite the verse.

So we, though many, are one body in Christ,
and individually members one of another.
Romans 12:5 ESV

Trace and copy the Scripture on the lines below.

...So we, though many, are one body in Christ,

and individually members one of another.

Now rewrite the verse.

Lesson 8

Let love be without dissimulation. Abhor that which is evil; cleave to that which is good. Be kindly affectioned one to another with brotherly love... Romans 12:9-10 KJV

Trace and copy the Scripture on the lines below.

Let love be without dissimulation. Abhor that which is

evil; cleave to that which is good. Be kindly affectioned

one to another with brotherly love.

Now rewrite the verse.

Let love be without hypocrisy. Abhor what is evil. Cling to what is good. Be kindly affectionate to one another with brotherly love...
Romans 12:9-10 NKJV

Trace and copy the Scripture on the lines below.

Let love be without hypocrisy. Abhor what is evil.

Cling to what is good. Be kindly affectionate to one

another with brotherly love...

Now rewrite the verse.

> *Your love must be real. Hate what is evil. Hold on to what is good.*
> *Love each other like brothers and sisters.*
> *Romans 12:9–10 JCB*

Trace and copy the Scripture on the lines below.

Your love must be real. Hate what is evil.

Hold on to what is good. Love each other

like brothers and sisters.

Now rewrite the verse.

> *Let love be genuine. Abhor what is evil; hold fast to what is good.*
> *Love one another with brotherly affection.*
> *Romans 12:9–10 ESV*

Trace and copy the Scripture on the lines below.

Let love be genuine. Abhor what is evil; hold fast to

what is good. Love one another with brotherly

affection.

Now rewrite the verse.

Lesson 9

...in honour preferring one another; not slothful in business;
fervent in spirit; serving the Lord;
Romans 12:10-11 KJV

Trace and copy the Scripture on the lines below.

...in honour preferring one another;

not slothful in business; fervent in spirit;

serving the Lord.

Now rewrite the verse.

...in honor giving preference to one another; not lagging in diligence,
fervent in spirit, serving the Lord;
Romans 12:10-11 NKJV

Trace and copy the Scripture on the lines below.

...in honor giving preference to one another; not lagging

in diligence, fervent in spirit, serving the Lord;

Now rewrite the verse.

> *Give your brothers and sisters more honor than you want*
> *for yourselves. Do not be lazy but work hard.*
> *Serve the Lord with all your heart.*
> *Romans 12:10–11 ICB*

Trace and copy the Scripture on the lines below.

Give your brothers and sisters more honor than you

want for yourselves. Do not be lazy but work hard.

Serve the Lord with all your heart.

Now rewrite the verse.

> *Outdo one another in showing honor. Do not be slothful in zeal,*
> *be fervent in spirit, serve the Lord.*
> *Romans 12:10–11 ESV*

Trace and copy the Scripture on the lines below.

Outdo one another in showing honor. Do not be

slothful in zeal, be fervent in spirit, serve the Lord.

Now rewrite the verse.

Lesson 10

> Be of the same mind one toward another.
> Romans 12:16 KJV

Trace and copy the Scripture on the lines below.

Be of the same mind one toward another.

Now rewrite the verse.

> Be of the same mind toward one another.
> Romans 12:16 NKJV

Trace and copy the Scripture on the lines below.

Be of the same mind toward one another.

Now rewrite the verse.

> Live together in peace with each other.
> Romans 12:16 ICB

Trace and copy the Scripture on the lines below.

Live together in peace with each other.

Now rewrite the verse.

Live in harmony with one another.
Romans 12:16 ESV

Trace and copy the Scripture on the lines below.

...Live in harmony with one another.

Now rewrite the verse.

Be of the same mind toward one another...
Romans 12:16 NASB

Trace and copy the Scripture on the lines below.

Be of the same mind toward one another...

Now rewrite the verse.

Lesson 11

Owe no man any thing, but to love one another:
for he that loveth another hath fulfilled the law.
Romans 13:8 KJV

Trace and copy the Scripture on the lines below.

Owe no man any thing, but to love one another:

for he that loveth another

hath fulfilled the law...

Now rewrite the verse.

Owe no one anything except to love one another,
for he who loves another has fulfilled the law.
Romans 12:16 NKJV

Trace and copy the Scripture on the lines below.

Owe no one anything except to love one another,

for he who loves another

has fulfilled the law.

Now rewrite the verse.

Do not owe people anything. But you will always owe love to each other. The person who loves others has obeyed all the law.
Romans 13:8 ICB

Trace and copy the Scripture on the lines below.

Do not owe people anything. But you will always owe

love to each other. The person who loves others has

obeyed all the law.

Now rewrite the verse.

Owe no one anything, except to love each other, for the one who loves another has fulfilled the law.
Romans 13:8 ESV

Trace and copy the Scripture on the lines below.

...Owe no one anything, except to love each other,

for the one who loves another

has fulfilled the law.

Now rewrite the verse.

Lesson 12

Let us not therefore judge one another any more: but judge this rather, that no man put a stumblingblock or an occasion to fall in his brother's way. Romans 14:13 KJV

Trace and copy the Scripture on the lines below.

Let us not therefore judge one another any more: but

judge this rather, that no man put a stumblingblock

or an occasion to fall in his brother's way.

Now rewrite the verse.

Therefore let us not judge one another anymore, but rather resolve this, not to put a stumbling block or a cause to fall in our brother's way. Romans 14:13 NKJV

Trace and copy the Scripture on the lines below.

Therefore let us not judge one another anymore, but

rather resolve this, not to put a stumbling block or

a cause to fall in our brother's way.

Now rewrite the verse.

So we should stop judging each other. We must make up our minds not to do anything that will make a Christian brother sin.
Romans 14:13 ICB

Trace and copy the Scripture on the lines below.

So we should stop judging each other. We must make

up our minds not to do anything that will make

a Christian brother sin.

Now rewrite the verse.

Therefore let us not pass judgment on one another any longer, but rather decide never to put a stumbling block or hindrance in the way of a brother. Romans 14:13 ESV

Trace and copy the Scripture on the lines below.

Therefore let us not pass judgment on one another

any longer, but rather decide never to put a

stumbling block or hindrance in the way of a brother.

Now rewrite the verse.

Lesson 13

> Wherefore receive ye one another,
> as Christ also received us to the glory of God.
> Romans 15:7 KJV

Trace and copy the Scripture on the lines below.

Wherefore receive ye one another,

as Christ also received us to the glory of God.

Now rewrite the verse.

> Therefore receive one another,
> just as Christ also received us, to the glory of God.
> Romans 15:7 NKJV

Trace and copy the Scripture on the lines below.

Therefore receive one another,

just as Christ also received us, to the glory of God.

Now rewrite the verse.

Christ accepted you, so you should accept each other.
This will bring glory to God.
Romans 15:7 ICB

Trace and copy the Scripture on the lines below.

Christ accepted you, so you should accept each other.

This will bring glory to God.

Now rewrite the verse.

Therefore welcome one another
as Christ has welcomed you, for the glory of God.
Romans 15:7 ESV

Trace and copy the Scripture on the lines below.

...Therefore welcome one another

as Christ has welcomed you, for the glory of God.

Now rewrite the verse.

Lesson 14

And I myself also am persuaded of you, my brethren, that ye also are full of goodness, filled with all knowledge, able also to admonish one another. Romans 15:14 KJV

Trace and copy the Scripture on the lines below.

And I myself also am persuaded of you, my brethren

that ye also are full of goodness, filled with all

knowledge, able also to admonish one another.

Now rewrite the verse.

Now I myself am confident concerning you, my brethren, that you also are full of goodness, filled with all knowledge, able also to admonish one another. Romans 15:14 NKJV

Trace and copy the Scripture on the lines below.

Now I myself am confident concerning you, my

brethren, that you also are full of goodness, filled with

all knowledge, able also to admonish one another.

Now rewrite the verse.

My brothers, I am sure that you are full of goodness.
I know that you have all the knowledge you need
and that you are able to teach each other. Romans 15:14 ICB

Trace and copy the Scripture on the lines below.

My brothers, I am sure that you are full of goodness.

I know that you have all the knowledge you need

and that you are able to teach each other.

Now rewrite the verse.

I myself am satisfied about you, my brothers, that you yourselves
are full of goodness, filled with all knowledge
and able to instruct one another. Romans 15:14 ESV

Trace and copy the Scripture on the lines below.

I myself am satisfied about you, my brothers, that

you yourselves are full of goodness, filled with all

knowledge and able to instruct one another.

Now rewrite the verse.

Lesson 15

Salute one another with an holy kiss.
The churches of Christ salute you.
Romans 16:16 KJV

Trace and copy the Scripture on the lines below.

Salute one another with an holy kiss.

The churches of Christ salute you.

Now rewrite the verse.

Greet one another with a holy kiss.
The churches of Christ greet you.
Romans 16:16 NKJV

Trace and copy the Scripture on the lines below.

Greet one another with a holy kiss.

The churches of Christ greet you.

Now rewrite the verse.

Greet each other with a holy kiss.
All of Christ's churches send greetings to you.
Romans 16:16 ICB

Trace and copy the Scripture on the lines below.

Greet each other with a holy kiss.

All of Christ's churches send greetings to you.

Now rewrite the verse.

Greet one another with a holy kiss.
All the churches of Christ greet you.
Romans 16:16 ESV

Trace and copy the Scripture on the lines below.

Greet one another with a holy kiss.

All the churches of Christ greet you.

Now rewrite the verse.

The Development of the Scriptures

The Bible we read today is made up of 66 books inspired by God, written and collected over many hundreds of years. These writings were originally written in three languages--Hebrew, Aramaic, and Greek--and were copied and translated by scribes, who passed them from generation to generation.

The following timeline shows the development of the books of the Bible in chronological order.

BOOK	WRITER	DATE	LANGUAGE
Genesis	Moses	1513 BC	Hebrew
Exodus	Moses	1512 BC	Hebrew
Leviticus	Moses	1512 BC	Hebrew
Job	Unknown	c. 1473 BC	Hebrew
Numbers	Moses	1473 BC	Hebrew
Deuteronomy	Moses	1473 BC	Hebrew
Joshua	Joshua	c. 1450 BC	Hebrew
Judges	Samuel	c. 1100 BC	Hebrew
Ruth	Samuel	c. 1090 BC	Hebrew
1 Samuel	Samuel, Gad, Nathan	c. 1078 BC	Hebrew
2 Samuel	Gad, Nathan	c. 1040 BC	Hebrew
Song of Solomon	Solomon	c. 1020 BC	Hebrew
Ecclesiastes	Solomon	b. 1000 BC	Hebrew
Jonah	Jonah	c. 844 BC	Hebrew
Joel	Joel	c. 820 BC	Hebrew
Amos	Amos	c. 804 BC	Hebrew
Hosea	Hosea	a. 745 BC	Hebrew
Isaiah	Isaiah	a. 732 BC	Hebrew
Micah	Micah	b. 717 BC	Hebrew
Proverbs	Solomon, Agur, Lemuel	c. 717 BC	Hebrew
Zephaniah	Zephaniah	b. 648 BC	Hebrew
Nahum	Nahum	b. 632 BC	Hebrew
Habakkuk	Habakkuk	c. 628 BC	Hebrew
Lamentations	Jeremiah	607 BC	Hebrew
Obadiah	Obadiah	c. 607 BC	Hebrew
Ezekiel	Ezekiel	c. 591 BC	Hebrew
1 and 2 Kings	Jeremiah	580 BC	Hebrew
Jeremiah	Jeremiah	580 BC	Hebrew
Daniel	Daniel	c. 536 BC	Hebrew, Aramaic
Haggai	Haggai	520 BC	Hebrew
Zechariah	Zechariah	518 BC	Hebrew
Esther	Mordecai	c. 475 BC	Hebrew

The Development of the Scriptures

B.C.: Before Christ
A.D.: *anno Domini* ("in the year of the Lord")

c.: circa (around)
a.: after
b.: before

BOOK	WRITER	DATE	LANGUAGE
1 and 2 Chronicles	Ezra	c. 460 BC	Hebrew
Ezra	Ezra	c. 460 BC	Hebrew, Aramaic
Psalms	David and others	c. 1000 to 460 BC	Hebrew
Nehemiah	Nehemiah	a. 443 BC	Hebrew
Malachi	Malachi	a. 443 BC	Hebrew
Matthew	Matthew	c. AD 41	Greek
1 Thessalonians	Paul	c. AD 51	Greek
2 Thessalonians	Paul	c. AD 52	Greek
Galatians	Paul	c. AD 50-52	Greek
1 Corinthians	Paul	c. AD 57	Greek
2 Corinthians	Paul	c. AD 58	Greek
Romans	Paul	c. AD 58	Greek
Luke	Luke	c. AD 56-58	Greek
Ephesians	Paul	c. AD 60-61	Greek
Colossians	Paul	c. AD 60-61	Greek
Philemon	Paul	c. AD 60-61	Greek
Philippians	Paul	c. AD 60-61	Greek
Hebrews	believed to be Paul	c. AD 61	Greek
Acts	Luke	c. AD 61	Greek
James	James (Jesus' brother)	b. AD 62	Greek
Mark	Mark	c. AD 60-65	Greek
1 Timothy	Paul	c. AD 61-65	Greek
Titus	Paul	c. AD 61-65	Greek
1 Peter	Peter	c. AD 62-64	Greek
2 Peter	Peter	c. AD 64	Greek
2 Timothy	Paul	c. AD 67	Greek
Jude	Jude (Jesus' brother)	c. AD 65	Greek
Revelation	Apostle John	c. AD 96	Greek
John	Apostle John	c. AD 98	Greek
1 John	Apostle John	c. AD 98	Greek
2 John	Apostle John	c. AD 98	Greek
3 John	Apostle John	c. AD 98	Greek

Lesson 16

Wherefore, my brethren, when ye come together to eat,
tarry one for another.
1 Corinthians 11:33 KJV

Trace and copy the Scripture on the lines below.

Wherefore, my brethren, when ye come together to eat,

tarry one for another.

Now rewrite the verse.

Therefore, my brethren, when you come together to eat,
wait for one another.
1 Corinthians 11:33 NKJV

Trace and copy the Scripture on the lines below.

Therefore, my brethren, when you come together to eat,

wait for one another.

Now rewrite the verse.

So my brothers, when you come together to eat,
wait for each other.
1 Corinthians 11:33 ICB

Trace and copy the Scripture on the lines below.

So my brothers, when you come together to eat,

wait for each other.

Now rewrite the verse.

So then, my brothers, when you come together to eat,
wait for one another.
1 Corinthians 11:33 ESV

Trace and copy the Scripture on the lines below.

So then, my brothers, when you come together to eat,

wait for one another.

Now rewrite the verse.

Lesson 17

That there should be no schism in the body;
but that the members should have the same care one for another.
1 Corinthians 12:25 KJV

Trace and copy the Scripture on the lines below.

That there should be no schism in the body; but that

the members should have the same care for one another.

Now rewrite the verse.

...that there should be no schism in the body,
but that the members should have the same care for one another.
1 Corinthians 12:25 NKJV

Trace and copy the Scripture on the lines below.

...that there should be no schism in the body, but that

the members should have the same care for one another.

Now rewrite the verse.

schism: a division between strongly opposed parties

> *God did this so that our body would not be divided.*
> *God wanted the different parts to care the same for each other.*
> *1 Corinthians 12:25 ICB*

Trace and copy the Scripture on the lines below.

God did this so that our body would not be divided. God

wanted the different parts to care the same for each other.

Now rewrite the verse.

> *...that there may be no division in the body,*
> *but that the members may have the same care for one another.*
> *1 Corinthians 12:25 ESV*

Trace and copy the Scripture on the lines below.

that there may be no division in the body, but that

the members may have the same care for one another.

Now rewrite the verse.

Lesson 18

All the brethren greet you.
Greet ye one another with an holy kiss.
1 Corinthians 16:20 KJV

Trace and copy the Scripture on the lines below.

All the brethren greet you.

Greet ye one another with an holy kiss.

Now rewrite the verse.

All the brethren greet you.
Greet one another with a holy kiss.
1 Corinthians 16:20 NKJV

Trace and copy the Scripture on the lines below.

All the brethren greet you.

Greet one another with a holy kiss.

Now rewrite the verse.

> *All the brothers here send greetings.*
> *Give each other a holy kiss when you meet.*
> *1 Corinthians 16:20 ICB*

Trace and copy the Scripture on the lines below.

All the brothers here send greetings.

Give each other a holy kiss when you meet.

Now rewrite the verse.

> *All the brothers send you greetings.*
> *Greet one another with a holy kiss.*
> *1 Corinthians 16:20 ESV*

Trace and copy the Scripture on the lines below.

All the brothers send you greetings.

Greet one another with a holy kiss.

Now rewrite the verse.

Lesson 19

Finally, brethren, farewell. Be perfect, be of good comfort, be of one mind, live in peace; and the God of love and peace shall be with you. 2 Corinthians 13:11 KJV

Trace and copy the Scripture on the lines below.

Finally, brethren, farewell. Be perfect, be of good comfort,

be of one mind, live in peace; and the God of love and

peace shall be with you.

Now rewrite the verse.

Finally, brethren, farewell. Become complete. Be of good comfort, be of one mind, live in peace; and the God of love and peace will be with you. 2 Corinthians 13:11 NKJV

Trace and copy the Scripture on the lines below.

Finally, brethren, farewell. Become complete. Be of good

comfort, be of one mind, live in peace; and the God of

love and peace will be with you.

Now rewrite the verse.

Now, brothers, I say goodbye. Live in harmony. Do what I have asked you to do. Agree with each other, and live in peace. Then the God of love and peace will be with you. 2 Corinthians 13:11 ICB

Trace and copy the Scripture on the lines below.

Now, brothers, I say goodbye. Live in harmony. Do what

I have asked you to do. Agree with each other, and live

in peace. Then the God of love and peace will be with you.

Now rewrite the verse.

Finally, brothers, rejoice. Aim for restoration, comfort one another, agree with one another, live in peace; and the God of love and peace will be with you. 2 Corinthians 13:11 ESV

Trace and copy the Scripture on the lines below.

Finally, brothers, rejoice. Aim for restoration, comfort one

another, agree with one another, live in peace; and the

God of love and peace will be with you.

Now rewrite the verse.

Lesson 20

For, brethren, ye have been called unto liberty; only use not liberty for an occasion to the flesh, but by love serve one another.
Galatians 5:13 KJV

Trace and copy the Scripture on the lines below.

For, brethren, ye have been called unto liberty; only
use not liberty for an occasion to the flesh, but by love
serve one another.

Now rewrite the verse.

For you, brethren, have been called to liberty; only do not use liberty as an opportunity for the flesh, but through love serve one another. Galatians 5:13 NKJV

Trace and copy the Scripture on the lines below.

For you, brethren, have been called to liberty; only do
not use liberty as an opportunity for the flesh, but
through love serve one another.

Now rewrite the verse.

My brothers, God called you to be free. But do not use your freedom as an excuse to do the things that please your sinful self. Serve each other with love. Galatians 5:13 ICB

Trace and copy the Scripture on the lines below.

My brothers, God called you to be free. But do not use

your freedom as an excuse to do the things that please

your sinful self. Serve each other with love.

Now rewrite the verse.

For you were called to freedom, brothers. Only do not use your freedom as an opportunity for the flesh, but through love serve one another. Galatians 5:13 ESV

Trace and copy the Scripture on the lines below.

For you were called to freedom, brothers. Only do not

use your freedom as an opportunity for the flesh, but

through love serve one another.

Now rewrite the verse.

Lesson 21

Let us not be desirous of vain glory,
provoking one another, envying one another.
Galatians 5:26 KJV

Trace and copy the Scripture on the lines below.

Let us not be desirous of vain glory, provoking one

another, envying one another.

Now rewrite the verse.

Let us not become conceited, provoking one another,
envying one another.
Galatians 5:26 NKJV

Trace and copy the Scripture on the lines below.

Let us not become conceited, provoking one another,

envying one another.

Now rewrite the verse.

We must not be proud. We must not make trouble with each other.
And we must not be jealous of each other.
Galatians 5:26 ICB

Trace and copy the Scripture on the lines below.

We must not be proud. We must not make trouble

with each other. And we must not be jealous of each other.

Now rewrite the verse.

Let us not become conceited, provoking one another,
envying one another.
Galatians 5:26 ESV

Trace and copy the Scripture on the lines below.

Let us not become conceited, provoking one another,

envying one another.

Now rewrite the verse.

Lesson 22

> Bear ye one another's burdens,
> and so fulfil the law of Christ.
> Galatians 6:2 KJV

Trace and copy the Scripture on the lines below.

Bear ye one another's burdens,

and so fulfil the law of Christ.

Now rewrite the verse.

> Bear one another's burdens,
> and so fulfill the law of Christ.
> Galatians 6:2 NKJV

Trace and copy the Scripture on the lines below.

Bear one another's burdens,

and so fulfill the law of Christ.

Now rewrite the verse.

Help each other with your troubles.
When you do this, you truly obey the law of Christ.
Galatians 6:2 ICB

Trace and copy the Scripture on the lines below.

Help each other with your troubles. When you do this,

you truly obey the law of Christ.

Now rewrite the verse.

Bear one another's burdens,
and so fulfill the law of Christ.
Galatians 6:2 ESV

Trace and copy the Scripture on the lines below.

Bear one another's burdens,

and so fulfill the law of Christ.

Now rewrite the verse.

Lesson 23

With all lowliness and meekness, with longsuffering,
forbearing one another in love...
Ephesians 4:2 KJV

Trace and copy the Scripture on the lines below.

With all lowliness and meekness, with longsuffering,

forbearing one another in love....

Now rewrite the verse.

...with all lowliness and gentleness, with longsuffering,
bearing with one another in love...
Ephesians 4:2 NKJV

Trace and copy the Scripture on the lines below.

...with all lowliness and gentleness, with longsuffering,

bearing with one another in love...

Now rewrite the verse.

Always be humble and gentle.
Be patient and accept each other with love.
Ephesians 4:2 ICB

Trace and copy the Scripture on the lines below.

Always be humble and gentle.

Be patient and accept each other with love.

Now rewrite the verse.

...with all humility and gentleness, with patience,
bearing with one another in love...
Ephesians 4:2 ESV

Trace and copy the Scripture on the lines below.

...with all humility and gentleness, with patience,

bearing with one another in love.

Now rewrite the verse.

Lesson 24

And be ye kind one to another, tenderhearted, forgiving one another,
even as God for Christ's sake hath forgiven you.
Ephesians 4:32 KJV

Trace and copy the Scripture on the lines below.

And be ye kind one to another, tenderhearted,

forgiving one another, even as God

for Christ's sake hath forgiven you.

Now rewrite the verse.

And be kind to one another, tenderhearted, forgiving one another,
even as God in Christ forgave you.
Ephesians 4:32 NKJV

Trace and copy the Scripture on the lines below.

And be kind to one another, tenderhearted, forgiving

one another, even as God in Christ forgave you.

Now rewrite the verse.

Be kind and loving to each other. Forgive each other just as God forgave you in Christ.
Ephesians 4:32 ICB

Trace and copy the Scripture on the lines below.

Be kind and loving to each other.

Forgive each other just as God forgave

you in Christ.

Now rewrite the verse.

Be kind to one another, tenderhearted, forgiving one another, as God in Christ forgave you.
Ephesians 4:32 ESV

Trace and copy the Scripture on the lines below.

Be kind to one another, tenderhearted, forgiving one

another, as God in Christ forgave you.

Now rewrite the verse.

Lesson 25

Speaking to yourselves in psalms and hymns and spiritual songs, singing and making melody in your heart to the Lord...
Ephesians 5:19 KJV

Trace and copy the Scripture on the lines below.

Speaking to yourselves in psalms and hymns and

spiritual songs, singing and making melody in your

heart to the Lord.

Now rewrite the verse.

...speaking to one another in psalms and hymns and spiritual songs, singing and making melody in your heart to the Lord...
Ephesians 5:19 NKJV

Trace and copy the Scripture on the lines below.

...speaking to one another in psalms and hymns and

spiritual songs, singing and making melody in your

heart to the Lord...

Now rewrite the verse.

Speak to each other with psalms, hymns, and spiritual songs.
Sing and make music in your hearts to the Lord.
Ephesians 5:19 ICB

Trace and copy the Scripture on the lines below.

Speak to each other with psalms, hymns, and

spiritual songs. Sing and make music in your

hearts to the Lord.

Now rewrite the verse.

...addressing one another in psalms and hymns and spiritual songs,
singing and making melody to the Lord with your heart...
Ephesians 5:19 ESV

Trace and copy the Scripture on the lines below.

...addressing one another in psalms and hymns and

spiritual songs, singing and making melody to the

Lord with your heart...

Now rewrite the verse.

Lesson 26

Submitting yourselves one to another in the fear of God.
Ephesians 5:21 KJV

Trace and copy the Scripture on the lines below.

Submitting yourselves one to another

in the fear of God.

Now rewrite the verse.

...submitting to one another in the fear of God.
Ephesians 5:21 NKJV

Trace and copy the Scripture on the lines below.

...submitting to one another

in the fear of God.

Now rewrite the verse.

Be willing to obey each other. Do this because you respect Christ.
Ephesians 5:21 ICB

Trace and copy the Scripture on the lines below.

Be willing to obey each other.

Do this because you respect Christ.

Now rewrite the verse.

...submitting to one another out of reverence for Christ.
Ephesians 5:21 ESV

Trace and copy the Scripture on the lines below.

...submitting to one another out of reverence

for Christ.

Now rewrite the verse.

Lesson 27

Let nothing be done through strife or vainglory;
but in lowliness of mind let each esteem other better than themselves.
Philippians 2:3 KJV

Trace and copy the Scripture on the lines below.

Let nothing be done through strife or vainglory;

but in lowliness of mind let each esteem other

better than themselves.

Now rewrite the verse.

Let nothing be done through selfish ambition or conceit,
but in lowliness of mind let each esteem others better than himself.
Philippians 2:3 NKJV

Trace and copy the Scripture on the lines below.

Let nothing be done through selfish ambition or conceit,

but in lowliness of mind let each esteem others better

than himself.

Now rewrite the verse.

When you do things, do not let selfishness or pride be your guide.
Be humble and give more honor to others than to yourselves.
Philippians 2:3 ICB

Trace and copy the Scripture on the lines below.

When you do things, do not let selfishness or pride be

your guide. Be humble and give more honor to others

than to yourselves.

Now rewrite the verse.

Do nothing from selfish ambition or conceit,
but in humility count others more significant than yourselves.
Philippians 2:3 ESV

Trace and copy the Scripture on the lines below.

Do nothing from selfish ambition or conceit,

but in humility count others more significant

than yourselves.

Now rewrite the verse.

Lesson 28

Lie not one to another, seeing that ye have
put off the old man with his deeds...
Colossians 3:9 KJV

Trace and copy the Scripture on the lines below.

Lie not one to another, seeing that ye have put off

the old man with his deeds...

Now rewrite the verse.

Do not lie to one another,
since you have put off the old man with his deeds...
Colossians 3:9 NKJV

Trace and copy the Scripture on the lines below.

Do not lie to one another, since you have put off the

old man with his deeds...

Now rewrite the verse.

Do not lie to each other. You have left your old sinful life
and the things you did before.
Colossians 3:9 ICB

Trace and copy the Scripture on the lines below.

Do not lie to each other. You have left your old

sinful life and the things you did before.

Now rewrite the verse.

Do not lie to one another, seeing that you have
put off the old self with its practices...
Colossians 3:9 ESV

Trace and copy the Scripture on the lines below.

Do not lie to one another, seeing that you have put

off the old self with its practices...

Now rewrite the verse.

Lesson 29

Forbearing one another, and forgiving one another, if any man have a quarrel against any: even as Christ forgave you, so also do ye.
Colossians 3:13 KJV

Trace and copy the Scripture on the lines below.

Forbearing one another, and forgiving one another, if

any man have a quarrel against any: even as Christ

forgave you, so also do ye.

Now rewrite the verse.

...bearing with one another, and forgiving one another, if anyone has a complaint against another; even as Christ forgave you, so you also must do. Colossians 3:13 NKJV

Trace and copy the Scripture on the lines below.

...bearing with one another, and forgiving one another,

if anyone has a complaint against another; even as

Christ forgave you, so you also must do.

Now rewrite the verse.

Do not be angry with each other, but forgive each other. If someone does wrong to you, then forgive him. Forgive each other because the Lord forgave you. Colossians 3:13 ICB

Trace and copy the Scripture on the lines below.

Do not be angry with each other, but forgive each other.

If someone does wrong to you, then forgive him.

Forgive each other because the Lord forgave you.

Now rewrite the verse.

...bearing with one another and, if one has a complaint against another, forgiving each other; as the Lord has forgiven you, so you also must forgive. Colossians 3:13 ESV

Trace and copy the Scripture on the lines below.

...bearing with one another and, if one has a complaint

against another, forgiving each other; as the Lord has

forgiven you, so you also must forgive.

Now rewrite the verse.

Lesson 30

Let the word of Christ dwell in you richly in all wisdom;
teaching and admonishing one another in psalms and hymns
and spiritual songs, singing with grace in your hearts to the Lord.
Colossians 3:16 KJV

Trace and copy the Scripture on the lines below.

Let the word of Christ dwell in you richly in all

wisdom teaching and admonishing one another in

psalms and hymns and spiritual songs, singing with

grace in your hearts to the Lord.

Now rewrite the verse.

> *Let the teaching of Christ live in you richly. Use all wisdom to teach and strengthen each other. Sing psalms, hymns, and spiritual songs with thankfulness in your hearts to God.*
> *Colossians 3:16 ICB*

Trace and copy the Scripture on the lines below.

Let the teaching of Christ live in you richly. Use all

wisdom to teach and strengthen each other. Sing psalms,

hymns, and spiritual songs with thankfulness in your

hearts to God.

Now rewrite the verse.

Translating the Scriptures

ORIGINAL LANGUAGES

The Scriptures were originally written in Hebrew, Aramaic, and Greek. Each of these languages uses a different alphabet.

Classical Hebrew

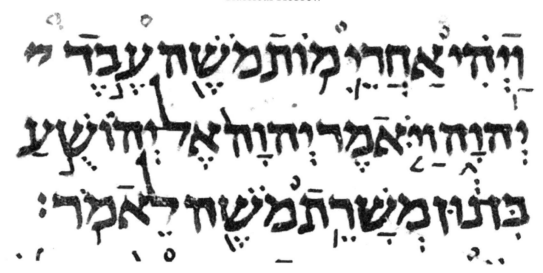

Biblical Aramaic

Biblical Greek

Translating the Scriptures

180 A.D. The New Testament starts to be translated from Greek into Latin, Syriac, and Coptic.

195 A.D. The name of the first translation of the Old and New Testaments into Latin was termed Old Latin, both Testaments having been translated from the Greek. Parts of the Old Latin were found in quotes by the church father Tertullian, who lived around 160-220 A.D. in north Africa and wrote treatises on theology.

300 A.D. The Old Syriac was a translation of the New Testament from the Greek into Syriac.

300 A.D. The Coptic Versions: Coptic was spoken in four dialects in Egypt. The Bible was translated into each of these four dialects.

380 A.D. The Latin Vulgate was translated by St. Jerome. He translated into Latin the Old Testament from the Hebrew and the New Testament from Greek. The Latin Vulgate became the Bible of the Western Church until the Protestant Reformation in the 1500's. It continues to be the authoritative translation of the Roman Catholic Church to this day.

1380 A.D. The first English translation of the Bible was by John Wycliffe. He translated the Bible into English from the Latin Vulgate. This was a translation from a translation and not a translation from the original Hebrew and Greek. Wycliffe was forced to translate from the Latin Vulgate because he did not know Hebrew or Greek.

1440s A. D. Gutenberg invents the printing press and publishes the Gutenberg Bible in the Latin Vulgate.

1500s A.D. The Protestant Reformation saw an increase in translations of the Bible into the common languages of the people.

1611 A.D. The King James Bible, translated from Greek, Hebrew, and Aramaic, is completed by 47 scholars for the Church of England, and replaced the Wycliffe Bible as the official English translation of the Bible.

Bible translation continues today! In the last fifty years, Bible scholars and translators have released many new English versions of the Bible, including the New King James Version, the English Standard Version, the New American Standard Bible, the New International Version, the New Living Translation, and many more. The Bible has also been translated into many languages around the world. According to Wycliffe Bible Translators, as of 2015:

- More than 1,300 languages have access to the New Testament and some portions of Scripture in their language.
- More than 550 languages have the complete translated Bible.
- About 7,000 languages are known to be in use today.
- Up to 180 million people need Bible translation to begin in their language.
- Just under 2,300 languages across 130 countries have active translation and linguistic development work happening right now.
- Up to 1,800 languages still need a Bible translation project to begin.

Lesson 31

And the Lord make you to increase and abound in love one toward another, and toward all men, even as we do toward you...
1 Thessalonians 3:12 KJV

Trace and copy the Scripture on the lines below.

And the Lord make you to increase and about in love

one toward another, and toward all men, even as we

do toward you...

Now rewrite the verse.

And may the Lord make you increase and abound in love to one another and to all, just as we do to you...
1 Thessalonians 3:12 NKJV

Trace and copy the Scripture on the lines below.

And may the Lord make you increase and abound in

love to one another and to all, just as we do to you...

Now rewrite the verse.

We pray that the Lord will make your love grow more and more for each other and for all people. We pray that you will love others as we love you... 1 Thessalonians 3:12 ICB

Trace and copy the Scripture on the lines below.

We pray that the Lord will make your love grow more

and more for each other and for all people. We pray

that you will love others as we love you.

Now rewrite the verse.

...and may the Lord make you increase and abound in love for one another and for all, as we do for you... 1 Thessalonians 3:12 ESV

Trace and copy the Scripture on the lines below.

...and may the Lord make you increase and abound in

love for one another and for all, as we do for you...

Now rewrite the verse.

Lesson 32

But as touching brotherly love ye need not that I write unto you:
for ye yourselves are taught of God to love one another.
1 Thessalonians 4:9 KJV

Trace and copy the Scripture on the lines below.

But as touching brotherly love ye need not that I

write unto you: for ye yourselves are taught of God to

love one another.

Now rewrite the verse.

But concerning brotherly love you have no need that I should write
to you, for you yourselves are taught by God to love one another.
1 Thessalonians 4:9 NKJV

Trace and copy the Scripture on the lines below.

But concerning brotherly love you have no need that

I should write to you, for you yourselves are taught

by God to love one another.

Now rewrite the verse.

> We do not need to write to you about having love for your brothers and sisters in Christ. God has already taught you to love each other.
> 1 Thessalonians 4:9 ICB

Trace and copy the Scripture on the lines below.

We do not need to write to you about having love for your brothers and sisters in Christ. God has already taught you to love each other.

Now rewrite the verse.

> Now concerning brotherly love you have no need for anyone to write to you, for you yourselves have been taught by God to love one another. 1 Thessalonians 4:9 ESV

Trace and copy the Scripture on the lines below.

Now concerning brotherly love you have no need for anyone to write to you, for you yourselves have been taught by God to love one another.

Now rewrite the verse.

Lesson 33

Wherefore comfort one another with these words.
1 Thessalonians 4:18 KJV

Trace and copy the Scripture on the lines below.

Wherefore comfort one another

with these words.

Now rewrite the verse.

Therefore comfort one another with these words...
1 Thessalonians 4:18 NKJV

Trace and copy the Scripture on the lines below.

Therefore comfort one another

with these words.

Now rewrite the verse.

So comfort each other with these words.
1 Thessalonians 4:18 ICB

Trace and copy the Scripture on the lines below.

So comfort each other

with these words.

Now rewrite the verse.

Therefore encourage one another with these words.
1 Thessalonians 4:18 ESV

Trace and copy the Scripture on the lines below.

Therefore encourage one another

with these words.

Now rewrite the verse.

Lesson 34

Wherefore comfort yourselves together, and edify one another,
eve[...]
1 Thess[...]

Trace and copy the Scripture on the lines below.

Wherefore comfort you[...]ly one

another, even as also[...]

Now rewrite the verse.

Therefore comfort each other and edify one another,
just as you also are doing.
1 Thessalonians 5:11 NKJV

Trace and copy the Scripture on the lines below.

Therefore comfort each other and edify one another,

just as you also are doing.

Now rewrite the verse.

So comfort each other and give each other strength,
just as you are doing now.
1 Thessalonians 5:11 ICB

Trace and copy the Scripture on the lines below.

So comfort each other and give each other strength, just

as you are doing now.

Now rewrite the verse.

Therefore encourage one another and build one another up,
just as you are doing.
1 Thessalonians 5:11 ESV

Trace and copy the Scripture on the lines below.

Therefore encourage one another and build one another

up, just as you are doing.

Now rewrite the verse.

Lesson 35

But exhort one another daily, while it is called To day;
lest any of you be hardened through the deceitfulness of sin.
Hebrews 3:13 KJV

Trace and copy the Scripture on the lines below.

But exhort one another daily, while it is called

To day; lest any of you be hardened through the

deceitfulness of sin.

Now rewrite the verse.

...but exhort one another daily, while it is called "Today,"
lest any of you be hardened through the deceitfulness of sin.
Hebrews 3:13 NKJV

Trace and copy the Scripture on the lines below.

...but exhort one another daily, while it is called "Today,"

lest any of you be hardened through the deceitfulness

of sin.

Now rewrite the verse.

But encourage each other every day. Do this while it is "today." Help each other so that none of you will become hardened because of sin and its tricks. Hebrews 3:13 ICB

Trace and copy the Scripture on the lines below.

But encourage each other every day. Do this while it is "today." Help each other so that none you will become hardened because of sin and its tricks.

Now rewrite the verse.

But exhort one another every day, as long as it is called "today," that none of you may be hardened by the deceitfulness of sin. Hebrews 3:13 ESV

Trace and copy the Scripture on the lines below.

But exhort one another every day, as long as it is called "today," that none of you may be hardened by the deceitfulness of sin.

Now rewrite the verse.

Lesson 36

And let us consider one another to provoke
unto love and to good works...
Hebrews 10:24 KJV

Trace and copy the Scripture on the lines below.

And let us consider one another to provoke

unto love and to good works...

Now rewrite the verse.

And let us consider one another in order
to stir up love and good works...
Hebrews 10:24 NKJV

Trace and copy the Scripture on the lines below.

And let us consider one another in order

to stir up love and good works...

Now rewrite the verse.

Let us think about each other and help each other
to show love and do good deeds.
Hebrews 10:24 ICB

Trace and copy the Scripture on the lines below.

Let us think about each other and help each other

to show love and do good deeds.

Now rewrite the verse.

And let us consider how to stir up one another
to love and good works...
Hebrews 10:24 ESV

Trace and copy the Scripture on the lines below.

And let us consider how to stir up one another

to love and good works...

Now rewrite the verse.

Lesson 37

Not forsaking the assembling of ourselves together, as the manner of some is; but exhorting one another: and so much the more, as ye see the day approaching. Hebrews 10:25 KJV

Trace and copy the Scripture on the lines below.

Not forsaking the assembling of ourselves together, as the

manner of some is; but exhorting one another: and so

much the more as ye see the day approaching.

Now rewrite the verse.

Not forsaking the assembling of ourselves together, as is the manner of some, but exhorting one another, and so much the more as you see the Day approaching. Hebrews 10:25 NKJV

Trace and copy the Scripture on the lines below.

...Not forsaking the assembling of ourselves together, as is

the manner of some, but exhorting one another, and so

much the more as you see the Day approaching.

Now rewrite the verse.

You should not stay away from the church meetings, as some are doing. But you should meet together and encourage each other. Do this even more as you see the Day coming. Hebrews 10:25 ICB

Trace and copy the Scripture on the lines below.

You should not stay away from the church meetings, as some are doing. But you should meet together and encourage each other. Do this even more as you see the Day coming.

Now rewrite the verse.

Lesson 38

Speak not evil one of another, brethren. He that speaketh evil of his brother, and judgeth his brother, speaketh evil of the law, and judgeth the law... James 4:11 KJV

Trace and copy the Scripture on the lines below.

Speak not evil one of another, brethren. He that speaketh evil of his brother, and judgeth his brother, speaketh evil of the law, and judgeth the law...

Now rewrite the verse.

Do not speak evil of one another, brethren. He who speaks evil of a brother and judges his brother, speaks evil of the law and judges the law. James 4:11 NKJV

Trace and copy the Scripture on the lines below.

Do not speak evil of one another, brethren. He who speaks evil of a brother and judges his brother, speaks evil of the law and judges the law.

Now rewrite the verse.

Brothers, do not say bad things about each other. If you say bad things about your brother in Christ or judge him, then you are saying bad things about the law... James 4:11 ICB

Trace and copy the Scripture on the lines below.

Brothers, do not say bad things about each other. If you

say bad things about your brother in Christ or judge

him, then you are saying bad things about the law...

Now rewrite the verse.

Do not speak evil against one another, brothers. The one who speaks against a brother or judges his brother, speaks evil against the law and judges the law. James 4:11 ESV

Trace and copy the Scripture on the lines below.

Do not speak evil against one another, brothers. The one

who speaks against a brother or judges his brother, speaks

evil against the law and judges the law.

Now rewrite the verse.

Lesson 39

Grudge not one against another,
brethren, lest ye be condemned...
James 5:9 KJV

Trace and copy the Scripture on the lines below.

Grudge not one against another,

brethren, lest ye be condemned...

Now rewrite the verse.

Do not grumble against one another, brethren,
lest you be condemned.
James 5:9 NKJV

Trace and copy the Scripture on the lines below.

Do not grumble against one another, brethren,

lest you be condemned.

Now rewrite the verse.

Brothers, do not complain against each other. If you do not stop complaining, you will be judged guilty.
James 5:9 ICB

Trace and copy the Scripture on the lines below.

Brothers, do not complain against each other. If you
do not stop complaining, you will be judged guilty.

Now rewrite the verse.

Do not grumble against one another, brothers,
so that you may not be judged...
James 5:9 ESV

Trace and copy the Scripture on the lines below.

Do not grumble against one another, brothers,
so that you may not be judged...

Now rewrite the verse.

Lesson 40

Confess your faults one to another, and pray one for another,
that ye may be healed.
James 5:16 KJV

Trace and copy the Scripture on the lines below.

Confess your faults one to another, and pray one for

another, that ye may be healed.

Now rewrite the verse.

Confess your trespasses to one another, and pray for one another,
that you may be healed.
James 5:16 NKJV

Trace and copy the Scripture on the lines below.

Confess your trespasses to one another, and pray for

one another, that you may be healed.

Now rewrite the verse.

> Confess your sins to each other and pray for each other.
> Do this so that God can heal you.
> James 5:16 ICB

Trace and copy the Scripture on the lines below.

Confess your sins to each other and pray for each other.

Do this so that God can heal you.

Now rewrite the verse.

> Therefore, confess your sins to one another and pray for one another,
> that you may be healed.
> James 5:16 ESV

Trace and copy the Scripture on the lines below.

Therefore, confess your sins to one another and pray

for one another, that you may be healed.

Now rewrite the verse.

Lesson 41

Finally, be ye all of one mind, having compassion one of another, love as brethren, be pitiful, be courteous...
1 Peter 3:8 KJV

Trace and copy the Scripture on the lines below.

Finally, be ye all of one mind, having compassion one

of another, love as brethren, be pitiful, be courteous...

Now rewrite the verse.

Finally, all of you be of one mind, having compassion for one another; love as brothers, be tenderhearted, be courteous...
1 Peter 3:8 NKJV

Trace and copy the Scripture on the lines below.

Finally, all of you be of one mind, having compassion

for one another; love as brothers, be tenderhearted, be

courteous...

Now rewrite the verse.

> *Finally, all of you should live together in peace. Try to understand each other. Love each other as brothers. Be kind and humble.*
> *1 Peter 3:8 ICB*

Trace and copy the Scripture on the lines below.

Finally, all of you should live together in peace. Try to understand each other. Love each other as brothers. Be kind and humble.

Now rewrite the verse.

> *Finally, all of you, have unity of mind, sympathy, brotherly love, a tender heart, and a humble mind.*
> *1 Peter 3:8 ESV*

Trace and copy the Scripture on the lines below.

Finally, all of you, have unity of mind, sympathy, brotherly love, a tender heart, and a humble mind.

Now rewrite the verse.

Lesson 42

And above all things have fervent charity among yourselves:
for charity shall cover the multitude of sins.
1 Peter 4:8 KJV

Trace and copy the Scripture on the lines below.

And above all things have fervent charity among

yourselves, for charity shall cover the multitude of sins.

Now rewrite the verse.

And above all things have fervent love for one another, for
"love will cover a multitude of sins."
1 Peter 4:8 NKJV

Trace and copy the Scripture on the lines below.

And above all things have fervent love for one another,

for "love will cover a multitude of sins."

Now rewrite the verse.

multitude: a large number

Most importantly, love each other deeply.
Love has a way of not looking at others' sins.
1 Peter 4:8 ICB

Trace and copy the Scripture on the lines below.

Most importantly, love each other deeply.

Love has a way of not looking at others' sins.

Now rewrite the verse.

Above all, keep loving one another earnestly,
since love covers a multitude of sins.
1 Peter 4:8 ESV

Trace and copy the Scripture on the lines below.

Above all, keep loving one another earnestly, since love

covers a multitude of sins.

Now rewrite the verse.

Lesson 43

Use hospitality one to another without grudging.
1 Peter 4:9 KJV

Trace and copy the Scripture on the lines below.

Use hospitality to one another

without grudging.

Now rewrite the verse.

Be hospitable to one another without grumbling.
1 Peter 4:9 NKJV

Trace and copy the Scripture on the lines below.

Be hospitable to one another

without grumbling.

Now rewrite the verse.

Open your homes to each other, without complaining.
1 Peter 4:9 ICB

Trace and copy the Scripture on the lines below.

Open your homes to each other,

without complaining.

Now rewrite the verse.

Be hospitable to one another without grumbling.
1 Peter 4:9 ESV

Trace and copy the Scripture on the lines below.

Be hospitable to one another

without grumbling.

Now rewrite the verse.

Lesson 44

As every man hath received the gift, even so minister the same one
to another, as good stewards of the manifold grace of God.
1 Peter 4:10 KJV

Trace and copy the Scripture on the lines below.

As every man hath received the gift, even so minister

the same one to another, as good stewards of the

manifold grace of God.

Now rewrite the verse.

steward: a person responsible to take care of something

As each one has received a gift, minister it to one another, as good
stewards of the manifold grace of God.
1 Peter 4:10 NKJV

Trace and copy the Scripture on the lines below.

As each one has received a gift, minister it to one

another, as good stewards of the manifold grace of God.

Now rewrite the verse.

Each of you received a spiritual gift. God has shown you his grace in giving you different gifts. And you are like servants who are responsible for using Gods gifts. So be good servants and use your gifts to serve each other. 1 Peter 4:10 ICB

Trace and copy the Scripture on the lines below.

Each of you received a spiritual gift. God has shown you

his grace in giving you different gifts. And you are like

servants who are responsible for using Gods gifts. So be

good servants and use your gifts to serve each other.

Now rewrite the verse.

As each has received a gift, use it to serve one another,
as good stewards of Gods varied grace...
1 Peter 4:10 ESV

Trace and copy the Scripture on the lines below.

As each has received a gift, use it to serve one another,

as good stewards of Gods varied grace...

Now rewrite the verse.

Lesson 45

> Likewise, ye younger, submit yourselves unto the elder. Yea, all of you be subject one to another, and be clothed with humility: for God resisteth the proud, and giveth grace to the humble.
> 1 Peter 5:5 KJV

Trace and copy the Scripture on the lines below.

Likewise, ye younger, submit yourselves unto the elder.

Yea, all of you be subject one to another, and be clothed

with humility: for God resisteth the proud, and giveth

grace to the humble.

Now rewrite the verse.

96

In the same way, younger men should be willing to be under older men. And all of you should be very humble with each other. "God is against the proud, but he gives grace to the humble."

1 Peter 5:5 ICB

Trace and copy the Scripture on the lines below.

In the same way, younger men should be willing to be

under older men. And all of you should be very

humble with each other. "God is against the proud, but

he gives grace to the humble.

Now rewrite the verse.

97

Copying the Scriptures

For nearly three thousand years, the Scriptures were written down and copied by hand. Scribes were very careful about copying each letter exactly from the original. The oldest copy of the Old Testament, the Dead Sea Scrolls, was discovered in 1947. The Dead Sea Scrolls were written in Hebrew.

The Dead Sea Scrolls

In the medieval period, monks copied the Bible in illuminated manuscripts. These artistic copies of the Scriptures include beautiful letters and pictures in many colors.

SCRIPTORIUM MONK AT WORK. (From *Lacroix*.)

Copying the Scriptures

Johannes Gutenberg invented the printing press in 1440. Several years later, he began printing the Gutenberg Bible, using the Latin Vulgate translation by St. Jerome. From this point on, many more people were able to read the Scriptures for themselves.

The Gutenberg Printing Press

The Gutenberg Bible

Lesson 46

For this is the message that ye heard from the beginning, that we should love one another.
1 John 3:11 KJV

Trace and copy the Scripture on the lines below.

For this is the message that ye heard from the

beginning, that we should love one another.

Now rewrite the verse.

For this is the message that you heard from the beginning, that we should love one another...
1 John 3:11 NKJV

Trace and copy the Scripture on the lines below.

For this is the message that you heard from the

beginning, that we should love one another...

Now rewrite the verse.

This is the teaching you have heard from the beginning:
We must love each other.
1 John 3:11 ICB

Trace and copy the Scripture on the lines below.

This is the teaching you have heard from the

beginning: We must love each other.

Now rewrite the verse.

For this is the message that you have heard from the beginning,
that we should love one another.
1 John 3:11 ESV

Trace and copy the Scripture on the lines below.

For this is the message that you have heard from the

beginning, that we should love one another.

Now rewrite the verse.

Lesson 47

And this is his commandment, That we should believe on the name of his Son Jesus Christ, and love one another, as he gave us commandment. 1 John 3:23 KJV

Trace and copy the Scripture on the lines below.

And this is his commandment, That we should believe

on the name of his Son Jesus Christ, and love one

another, as he gave us commandment.

Now rewrite the verse.

And this is His commandment: that we should believe on the name of His Son Jesus Christ and love one another, as He gave us commandment. 1 John 3:23 NKJV

Trace and copy the Scripture on the lines below.

And this is His commandment: that we should believe

on the name of His Son Jesus Christ and love one

another, as He gave us commandment.

Now rewrite the verse.

This is what God commands: that we believe in his Son,
Jesus Christ, and that we love each other, just as he commanded.
1 John 3:23 ICB

Trace and copy the Scripture on the lines below.

This is what God commands: that we believe in his

Son, Jesus Christ, and that we love each other, just as

he commanded.

Now rewrite the verse.

And this is his commandment, that we believe in the name of his
Son Jesus Christ and love one another, just as he has
commanded us.   1 John 3:23 ESV

Trace and copy the Scripture on the lines below.

And this is his commandment, that we believe in the

name of his Son Jesus Christ and love one another,

just as he has commanded us.

Now rewrite the verse.

Lesson 48

Beloved, let us love one another: for love is of God;
and every one that loveth is born of God, and knoweth God.
1 John 4:7 KJV

Trace and copy the Scripture on the lines below.

Beloved, let us love one another: for love is of God; and

every one that loveth is born of God, and knoweth God.

Now rewrite the verse.

Beloved, let us love one another, for love is of God;
and everyone who loves is born of God and knows God.
1 John 4:7 NKJV

Trace and copy the Scripture on the lines below.

Beloved, let us love one another, for love is of God; and

everyone who loves is born of God and knows God.

Now rewrite the verse.

Dear friends, we should love each other, because love comes from God. The person who loves has become God's child and knows God.
1 John 4:7 ICB

Trace and copy the Scripture on the lines below.

Dear friends, we should love each other, because love

comes from God. The person who loves has become God's

child and knows God.

Now rewrite the verse.

Beloved, let us love one another, for love is from God, and whoever loves has been born of God and knows God.
1 John 4:7 ESV

Trace and copy the Scripture on the lines below.

Beloved, let us love one another, for love is from God,

and whoever loves has been born of God and knows God.

Now rewrite the verse.

Lesson 49

Beloved, if God so loved us, we ought also to love one another. No man hath seen God at any time. If we love one another, God dwelleth in us, and his love is perfected in us.
1 John 4:11-12 KJV

Trace and copy the Scripture on the lines below.

Beloved, if God so loved us, we ought also to love one another. No man hath seen God at any time. If we love one another, God dwelleth in us, and his love is perfected in us.

Now rewrite the verse.

That is how much God loved us, dear friends! So we also must love each other. No one has ever seen God. But if we love each other, God lives in us. If we love each other, God's love has reached its goal. It is made perfect in us. 1 John 4:11–12 ICB

Trace and copy the Scripture on the lines below.

That is how much God loved us, dear friends! So we also

must love each other. No one has ever seen God. But if

we love each other, God lives in us. If we love each other,

God's love has reached its goal. It is made perfect in us.

Now rewrite the verse.

Lesson 50

And now I beseech thee, lady, not as though I wrote a new commandment unto thee, but that which we had from the beginning, that we love one another. 2 John 1:5 KJV

Trace and copy the Scripture on the lines below.

And now I beseech thee, lady, not as though I wrote a new commandment unto thee, but that which we had from the beginning, that we love one another.

Now rewrite the verse.

And now I plead with you, lady, not as though I wrote a new commandment to you, but that which we have had from the beginning: that we love one another. 2 John 1:5 NKJV

Trace and copy the Scripture on the lines below.

And now I plead with you, lady, not as though I wrote a new commandment to you, but that which we have had from the beginning: that we love one another.

Now rewrite the verse.

And now, dear lady, I tell you: We should all love each other. This is not a new command. It is the same command we have had from the beginning. 2 John 1:5 ICB

Trace and copy the Scripture on the lines below.

And now, dear lady, I tell you: We should all love each other. This is not a new command. It is the same command we have had from the beginning.

Now rewrite the verse.

And now I ask you, dear lady--not as though I were writing you a new commandment, but the one we have had from the beginning--that we love one another. 2 John 1:5 ESV

Trace and copy the Scripture on the lines below.

And now I ask you, dear lady---not as thought I were writing you a new commandment, but the one we have had from the beginning---that we love one another.

Now rewrite the verse.

Items available from Laurelwood Books:

Ōlim, Once Upon a Time, in Latin Series:
Book I (reader and workbook): The Three Little Pigs, The Tortoise and the Hare,
The Crow and the Pitcher
Book II (reader and workbook): The Ant and the Chrysalis, The Lost Sheep,
The Good Samaritan
Book III (reader and workbook) - The Feeding of the 5,000, The Lion and the Mouse
Book IV (reader and workbook) - Creation
Book V (reader and workbook) - Daniel, Part I; We Know a Tree by its Fruit
Book VI (reader and workbook) - The Prodigal Son
book VII (reader and workbook) - David and Goliath
Book VIII (reader and workbook) - Daniel, Part II
Book IX (reader and workbook) - Daniel, Part III, The Miser
Book X (reader and workbook) - The Wise Man and Foolish Man, The Ten Maidens

Ōlim Derivatives I
Ōlim Derivatives II (Coming Soon)

Scripture Scribes Series
Primary: *His Name Is Wonderful*
Intermediate: *One Another*
Upper School: *Men of Honor & Women of Grace*

Patriotic Penmanship Series for Grades K-12
Also Available: Jump Rope Review Book, Transition to Cursive Book,
Dinosaur Review Book

State The Facts: A Guide to Studying Your State Whether you are studying the state you
live in or any other state, this book offers your student the opportunity to research and
learn state history, geography, weather, and more!

Study Guides:
Based on Rosemary Sutcliff's historical fiction
*The Eagle of the Ninth • The Silver Branch Outcast • The Lantern Bearers
Warrior Scarlet • Sword Song • The Shining Company*

Based on Emma Leslie's historical fiction:
*Out of the Mouth of the Lion
Glaucia the Greek Slave*

Laurelwood Books offers both new and used curricula to families wishing
to help their children learn and achieve success in school or at home.

To order: www.laurelwoodbooks.com
laurelwoodbooks@earthlink.net

55923460R00062

Made in the USA
Charleston, SC
09 May 2016